Spring Harvest Bible Workbook

United:
Reflections on the church and living a Christ-inspired lifestyle

Ephesians

British Library Cataloguing in Publication Data

A catalogue record for this book is available from the British Library

ISBN 978-1-899788-82-8

Typeset by Ascent Creative
Cover design by Paul Lewis Design
Printed by Halcyon

Contents

About this book

This book is written primarily for use in a group situation, but can easily be used by individuals who want to study the book of Ephesians. It can be used in a variety of contexts, so it is perhaps helpful to spell out the assumptions that we have made about the groups that will use it. These can have a variety of names – homegroups, Bible study groups, cell groups – we've used group as the generic term.

- The emphasis of the studies will be on the application of the Bible. Group members will not just learn facts, but will be encouraged to think 'How does this apply to me? What change does it require of me? What incidents or situations in my life is this relevant to?'

- Groups can encourage honesty and make space for questions and doubts. The aim of the studies is not to find the 'right answer', but to help members understand the Bible by working through their questions. The Christian faith throws up paradoxes. Events in people's lives may make particular verses difficult to understand. The group should be a safe place to express these concerns.

- Groups can give opportunities for deep friendships to develop. Group members will be encouraged to talk about their experiences, feelings, questions, hopes and fears. They will be able to offer one another pastoral support and to get involved in each other's lives.

- There is a difference between being a collection of individuals who happen to meet together every Wednesday and being an effective group who bounce ideas off each other, spark inspiration and creativity, pooling their talents and resources to create solutions together: one whose whole is definitely greater than the sum of its parts. The process of working through these studies will encourage healthy group dynamics.

Space is given for you to write answers, comments, questions and thoughts. This book will not tell you what to think, but will help you discover the truth of God's word through thinking, discussing, praying and listening.

FOR GROUP MEMBERS

- You will probably get more out of the study if you spend some time during the week reading the passage and thinking about the questions. Make a note of anything you don't understand.

- Pray that God will help you to understand the passage and show you how to apply it. Pray for other members in the group too, that they will find the study helpful.

- Be willing to take part in the discussions. The leader of the group is not there as an expert with all the answers. They will want everyone to get involved and share their thoughts and opinions.

- However, don't dominate the group! If you are aware that you are saying a lot, make space for others to contribute. Be sensitive to other group members and aim to be encouraging. If you disagree with someone, say so but without putting down their contribution.

FOR INDIVIDUALS

- Although this book is written with a group in mind, it can also be easily used by individuals. You obviously won't be able to do the group activities suggested, but you can consider how you would answer the questions and write your thoughts in the space provided.

- You may find it helpful to talk to a prayer partner about what you have learnt, and ask them to pray for you as you try and apply what you are learning to your life.

- The New International Version of the text is printed in the book. If you use a different version, then read from your own Bible as well.

Introduction to EPHESIANS

Read first!

Reading Paul's letter to the Ephesians is like sitting down to a rich banquet – there's just so much in it, it can be hard to take it all in at once. Paul starts with an explosion of praise for all that Jesus has done for us, describing with complete confidence our identity in Christ that needs to be the foundation for who we are and what we do. He celebrates the unity that Jesus brings to Jews and Gentiles, breaking down the dividing walls between us and bringing us together to be a dwelling for God. He talks about the great transformation that Jesus has brought about in our lives and how that needs to be expressed in the way we live. He gets on his knees to pray fervently that the Ephesians would know more of the love of Christ.

And he talks with great excitement about the role of the Church as a people movement that is called to impact the world. He declares that the Church is not an accident of history, but the fulfilment of God's long-held plans and the new expression of what God has always purposed. He refers to the mystery long-hidden in the heart of God, but now made plain that 'through the Church the manifold wisdom of God should be made known to the rulers and authorities in the heavenly realms' (Ephesians 3:10). The Church, says Paul, is God's brilliant idea, and we are an essential part of it.

In these sessions we'll be exploring some of the metaphors that Paul uses in Ephesians to describe the Church, which help us understand the heart of God's intention in entrusting us with the spread of his kingdom. We'll consider the Church as:

1. the people of God, secure in their identity and involved in the mission of God

2. the bride of Christ, a diverse community who are committed to learning from each other

3. the body of Christ, being Jesus to the world around us

4. the community of the Spirit, transformed by God dwelling in us rather than our own efforts.

These metaphors will help us to see not only what the Church is, but what it can be.

As Gerard Kelly says: 'The Church is God's brilliant idea, and at its best it is the most remarkable, the most colourful, the most beautiful and the most redeeming of all

Read out.

communities. It is a community of welcome and of healing, of forgiveness and of the second chance, a place of unexpected joy and unearned grace. At its best it is the family we all want and need. At its worst, it is the family we run from, the dysfunctional, controlling horror show that haunts our nights and ruins our days. But the answer to dysfunction does not lie in living alone. We will not be healed by running from relationship. Rather it is in building healthy churches, in creating communities of self-giving love, that we will find hope for ourselves and for our world.'

As you study this wonderful letter to the Ephesians, pray that God will inspire you with his vision for all the Church can be, and equip you to play your part in making that a reality.

Session 1: People of God

 AIM: To enable people to have a stronger sense of their identity in Christ that fuels their involvement in the mission of God

TO SET THE SCENE

Think of three ways of describing yourself beginning with the words 'I am...' You could choose surprising things that people don't know about you, or simple facts about yourself such as what you do and where you come from. Share these with the rest of the group.

Take some time to look at the story in front of you, making sure that, as a group, you all understand how the pieces fit together.

READ THE PASSAGE TOGETHER:

1 [1]*Paul, an apostle of Christ Jesus by the will of God, To God's holy people in Ephesus, the faithful in Christ Jesus:*

[2]*Grace and peace to you from God our Father and the Lord Jesus Christ.*

may not always be materially blessed.

[3]*Praise be to the God and Father of our Lord Jesus Christ, who has blessed us in the heavenly realms with every spiritual blessing in Christ. [4]For he chose us in him before the creation of the world to be holy and blameless in his sight. In love [5]he predestined us for adoption to sonship through Jesus Christ, in accordance with his pleasure and will— [6]to the praise of his glorious grace, which he has freely given us in the One he loves. [7]In him we have redemption through his blood, the forgiveness of sins, in accordance with the riches of God's grace [8]that he lavished on us. With all wisdom and understanding, [9]he made known to us the mystery of his will according to his good pleasure, which he purposed in Christ, [10]to be put into effect when the times reach their fulfillment—to bring unity to all things in heaven and on earth under Christ.*

[11]*In him we were also chosen, having been predestined according to the plan of him who works out everything in conformity with the purpose of his will, [12]in order that we, who were the first to put our hope in Christ, might be for the praise of his glory. [13]And you also were included in Christ when you heard the message of truth, the gospel of your salvation. When you believed, you were marked in him with a seal,*

the promised Holy Spirit, [14]who is a deposit guaranteeing our inheritance until the redemption of those who are God's possession—to the praise of his glory.

[15]For this reason, ever since I heard about your faith in the Lord Jesus and your love for all God's people, [16]I have not stopped giving thanks for you, remembering you in my prayers. [17]I keep asking that the God of our Lord Jesus Christ, the glorious Father, may give you the Spirit of wisdom and revelation, so that you may know him better. [18]I pray that the eyes of your heart may be enlightened in order that you may know the hope to which he has called you, the riches of his glorious inheritance in his holy people, [19]and his incomparably great power for us who believe. That power is the same as the mighty strength [20]he exerted when he raised Christ from the dead and seated him at his right hand in the heavenly realms, [21]far above all rule and authority, power and dominion, and every name that is invoked, not only in the present age but also in the one to come. [22]And God placed all things under his feet and appointed him to be head over everything for the church, [23]which is his body, the fullness of him who fills everything in every way.

2 [1]As for you, you were dead in your transgressions and sins, [2]in which you used to live when you followed the ways of this world and of the ruler of the kingdom of the air, the spirit who is now at work in those who are disobedient. [3]All of us also lived among them at one time, gratifying the cravings of our flesh and following its desires and thoughts. Like the rest, we were by nature deserving of wrath. [4]But because of his great love for us, God, who is rich in mercy, [5]made us alive with Christ even when we were dead in transgressions—it is by grace you have been saved. [6]And God raised us up with Christ and seated us with him in the heavenly realms in Christ Jesus, [7]in order that in the coming ages he might show the incomparable riches of his grace, expressed in his kindness to us in Christ Jesus. [8]For it is by grace you have been saved, through faith—and this is not from yourselves, it is the gift of God— [9]not by works, so that no one can boast. [10]For we are God's handiwork, created in Christ Jesus to do good works, which God prepared in advance for us to do.

Ephesians 1:1-2:10

Paul addresses this letter to God's holy people in Ephesus. But these words are for us too - we are the people of God, belonging to God and loved by him. Paul then launches into a rich description of who we are in Christ and all that God has done for us – a description so rich that it can be hard to take in when you first read it. It's like sitting down to an opulent banquet and being overwhelmed by the quantity and quality of the food being offered. If you tried to eat it all at once, it would just be too much; but taking in a bit at a time nourishes and strengthens you. Paul wants us to be secure in our identity in Christ so that we can then get on with the work that God has prepared for us to do.

DISCUSS TOGETHER

1. Read verse one again. What does the phrase 'the people of God' mean to you? What does it say about us? What does it say about God?

 2. In verses 3 to 14, Paul writes about who we are in Christ and what God has done for us. In the margin of this book, make a list of what these verses say about you starting each phrase with the words 'I am...' So verse 3 says 'I am blessed; verse 4 says 'I am chosen; I am holy; I am blameless' and so on.

Then compare your lists as a group, making sure you haven't missed anything!

This is your identity in Christ. How real is this to you? On a scale of 1 to 10, where 1 is 'hardly' and 10 is 'totally', how much do you feel you own this identity?

Am I a Son of God?

In verse 5 Paul says we are chosen by God for adoption to sonship through Jesus. The Greek word for 'adoption to sonship' is a legal term referring to the full legal standing of an adopted male heir in Roman culture. So that phrase doesn't mean that we all become male in Christ, but that all of us, both men and women, have the same rights, status and responsibilities as joint heirs of God.

 3. Now invite someone to read the list again but starting each phrase with the words 'We are...', and thinking about your church as a whole. How much do you think your church owns this identity in Christ? What would help them to own it more? How might your church be different if every member were secure in this identity?

 4. Paul prays that the people of God would know him better. What three things does he specifically pray for in verses 18 and 19? Why do you think he chooses these three?

We are chosen, we are holy = set apart, different
He's omnipotent, by his will ... in charge of wor
3. I am blessed
4. we are chosen, holy + blameless in his ey
5. I am loved, his daughter
6. I am full of his grace free gift
7. I am 4given, redeemed
10. I am part of united bod of church in heaven + ea
13. I am included
14. -- marked with seal, HS

dont · Fractured · Factions
Holy Spirit, doing things toge
prayer street walking
More united, more cooperative, less faction
One goal - enjoy God + brin
others to him. Martha/Mary

1 enlightenment
2 knowledge of our callin we can
3 empowerment task for
1 cant understand what f
about if hearts closed
2 have to be certain to be
3 need power of HS to be

What does the Bible say?

5. Read verses 20-23. Jesus is far above all rule and authority, head over everything. Name some of the powers and authority in our world that Jesus rules over. What does this mean for us? ?

6. In Ephesians 2:1-7, Paul contrasts what we were before we knew Christ, and what we are now. Half the group make a list of how Paul describes the 'before', and half make a list of how he describes the 'after'. Then one by one read out contrasting statements of the 'before' and 'after', as a collective declaration of faith. You could begin with 'We used to be dead' from one half of the group, and 'but God has made us alive with Christ because of his great love for us' from the other. Discuss.

Again, discuss how real this new identity feels for each of you. How can you grow more into the reality of the 'after'?

What does the Bible say?

7. How have we been saved according to 2:8? Talk about the difference between being saved by grace and saved by works. How might someone behave and feel who thinks they have been saved by works? How might someone behave and feel who knows they have been saved by grace? What is grace? unmerited gift.

8. Having focused on what God has done and encouraged people to be secure in their identity in Christ, Paul ends this section of Ephesians with a declaration of our purpose in 2:10 – what is it? do good works God prepd. for us.

Later in Ephesians, Paul says that the wisdom of God will be made known to the world through the church (Ephesians 3:10). The good work that God has prepared for us is to take part in the mission of God, allowing God to act in us and through us for the redemption of the world. see back

One definition of mission is captured in the prayer that Jesus taught in Matthew 5: 'Your

My thoughts and notes....

Above Al Qaeda, Islam + all man-made institutions
Jesus above them – not of ultimate imp. Will pass.
Jesus is Head of + rules his church.

see my notes.
Write befores + afters on slips.

Everyday remind myself of who I am in Christ.
ph. copy from Freedom in Christ. Ask for HS.

Free gift ∴ God is kind
driven to always do more?
insecure, have I done enough? (Islam) superior?
- confident, secure, God is pleased with me; don't need to compare myself with anyone, see myself as superior or inferior to anyone

...be faithful + keep going
...ective.

kingdom come, your will be done, on earth as in heaven.' Wherever the will of God is not done on earth, there is scope for mission. Wherever the will of God is done where it was not before, then more of the mission of God has been fulfilled. Do you find this definition helpful?

yes!

 What about my church? **9.** On a local map, mark the spheres of influence of members of the group. Stick different coloured pins in the map to help you. Spheres of influence might include where people work, where they live, where they volunteer, clubs they belong to, where they study or teach. What does this map show you about how your group might engage in the mission of God?

WORSHIP

Spread out some of the phrases that describe what we were like before we knew Christ, from Ephesians 2:1-3. Take it in turns to pray, choosing one of these phrases and transforming it into what God has done for us in Jesus. Pray that this new identity would become a firm reality for everyone in the group. Pray that out of that identity, you would be able to take part in the mission of God, doing the good works that God has prepared for each of you.

DURING THE WEEK

Spend some time meditating on your identity in Christ, using the phrases from this passage of Ephesians that you have highlighted in this session. Compare these phrases to what you normally say or feel about yourself. Ask God to transform your thinking so that you are able to fully own your identity in Christ. Use this as a springboard for praise and worship for all that God has done and is doing in your life.

✕ FOR FURTHER STUDY ✕

Read through the whole of the book of Ephesians, to get a sense of Paul's excitement at what God has done for us and what that will lead to if we grasp hold of it fully.

Read John Stott's commentary on Ephesians to really dig deep into this book - *The Message of Ephesians: God's New Society* by John Stott (IVP)

Introducing the Missional Church by Alan Roxborough (Baker Books) is a very practical book that explores what it means for a church to be missional and then outlines a process to follow to make that shift.

Session 2: Bride of Christ

◎ **AIM: To understand the global, diverse nature of the church and our need to listen and learn from each other in order to fully encounter Christ.**

TO SET THE SCENE

Talk about the experiences of other cultures that you have had in the last month or so. You might include places you've visited, meals you've eaten, friends and neighbours you have connected with, arts and entertainment you've enjoyed and happenings in the local community.

READ THE PASSAGE TOGETHER:

2 *¹¹Therefore, remember that formerly you who are Gentiles by birth and called "uncircumcised" by those who call themselves "the circumcision" (which is done in the body by human hands)— ¹²remember that at that time you were separate from Christ, excluded from citizenship in Israel and foreigners to the covenants of the promise, without hope and without God in the world. ¹³But now in Christ Jesus you who once were far away have been brought near by the blood of Christ.*

¹⁴For he himself is our peace, who has made the two groups one and has destroyed the barrier, the dividing wall of hostility, ¹⁵by setting aside in his flesh the law with its commands and regulations. His purpose was to create in himself one new humanity out of the two, thus making peace, ¹⁶and in one body to reconcile both of them to God through the cross, by which he put to death their hostility. ¹⁷He came and preached peace to you who were far away and peace to those who were near. ¹⁸For through him we both have access to the Father by one Spirit.

¹⁹Consequently, you are no longer foreigners and strangers, but fellow citizens with God's people and also members of his household, ²⁰built on the foundation of the apostles and prophets, with Christ Jesus himself as the chief cornerstone. ²¹In him the whole building is joined together and rises to become a holy temple in the Lord. ²²And in him you too are being built together to become a dwelling in which God lives by his Spirit.

3 *¹For this reason I, Paul, the prisoner of Christ Jesus for the sake of you Gentiles— ²Surely you have heard about the administration of God's grace that was given to me for you, ³that is, the mystery made known to me by revelation, as*

I have already written briefly. ⁴In reading this, then, you will be able to understand my insight into the mystery of Christ, ⁵which was not made known to people in other generations as it has now been revealed by the Spirit to God's holy apostles and prophets. ⁶This mystery is that through the gospel the Gentiles are heirs together with Israel, members together of one body, and sharers together in the promise in Christ Jesus.

⁷I became a servant of this gospel by the gift of God's grace given me through the working of his power. ⁸Although I am less than the least of all the Lord's people, this grace was given me: to preach to the Gentiles the boundless riches of Christ, ⁹and to make plain to everyone the administration of this mystery, which for ages past was kept hidden in God, who created all things. ¹⁰His intent was that now, through the church, the manifold wisdom of God should be made known to the rulers and authorities in the heavenly realms, ¹¹according to his eternal purpose that he accomplished in Christ Jesus our Lord. ¹²In him and through faith in him we may approach God with freedom and confidence. ¹³I ask you, therefore, not to be discouraged because of my sufferings for you, which are your glory.

Ephesians 2:11-3:13

My thoughts and notes....

Our familiarity with the gospel being for all people means that we probably miss the impact of Paul's practice in the early church, where he included the Gentiles in his teaching, evangelism and the churches he was linked to. As a Pharisee he would have been taught from infancy to fear and despise Gentile culture, and he would have thanked God in prayer every day that he was not a Gentile. His encounter with Jesus on the road to Damascus completely transformed that view and in these verses, Paul talks about his calling to the Gentiles and the mystery that the Jews and the Gentiles are heirs together of the kingdom.

Later, in Ephesians 5:32, Paul uses the metaphor of marriage to describe the relationship between Christ and the Church. And in Revelation John talks explicitly about the Church being the Bride of Christ (see Revelation19:7, 21:2, 21:9 and 22:17), drawn from every nation, tribe, people and language (Revelation 7:9). The image of the Bride of Christ is a measure of the overwhelming love of God for all human beings across the globe.

God is drawing together a truly global family; all the colours of humanity will be present in God's bride.

DISCUSS TOGETHER

 1. Paul is pretty clear in Ephesians 2:11-22 that the division between Jews and Gentiles is abolished in Christ. What phrases does he use in these verses to spell it out?

2. Before the birth of Jesus, how would the Jews have understood God's plan of salvation for the world? Can you think of examples of where Jesus began to challenge this view in his ministry?

 3. And now Paul talks about a mystery being revealed that will radically alter the Jewish worldview – what is that mystery (3:2-11)? What role does the church have to play in that mystery?

4. What are some of the challenges of bringing together into one church two very different groups of people like the Jews and the Gentiles? And what are some of the benefits? What attitudes do people need for it to work?

Engaging with the world **5.** What divisions exist in our society that parallel the split between Jews and Gentiles in Paul's day? What would reconciliation between those groups look like? How might these verses from Ephesians impact the way we relate to or pray for those groups?

6. Missiologist Andrew Walls talks about the 'Ephesian moment' – the fact that in Ephesus Christians of two very different cultures could have formed two separate churches, but they did not. The two cultures coming together created a richer, fuller understanding and expression of who Jesus is than if they had stayed apart, as they learned from each other. He suggests that we face another 'Ephesian moment' now as we

Handwritten notes:

Do 1, 2, 3, 7

13. brought near
14. made the 2 one
   - destroyed barrier
15. create in himself o
15 new man out of 2
16. reconcile both to c
18. thro' him both have all
19. fellow citizens
19. members of God's household
22. built together

Gentiles are include now. our job to tell people Jesus loves them too.

different way of relating to God. Don't assume or way is only right way. village church include high + low church people feeling stat - different way to worship - discu

mystery of God can only be reveal by the HS. Can't work it out ourselves. Study Bible + theolo but only HS enables us to know God. mystery of God only revealed thro Jesus in NT.

Abraham

Centurion's daugh Samaritan woman

see v10.

Humility. acceptance, teachability

have the opportunity to learn from expressions of Christian faith from around the globe. What do you think of this idea? What opportunities have you had to learn from Christians and theologians from other cultures? How might you create those opportunities?

 7. Take a moment to reflect on the ethnic mix of the city or community in which you live. How many distinct language groups or cultures are represented there? Now repeat the exercise for your church. Compare the two lists; who from the first is missing from the second? What can you do to change this?

 8. A growing number of church leaders are talking about building intercultural churches that actively seek dialogue between different cultures and encourage learning from each other. An intercultural church not only attracts people from diverse cultural backgrounds, but seeks input and involvement from those cultures. How might this approach impact:

▶ the language you use in services and prayers?

▶ the musical styles of worship?

▶ the pattern of worship services?

▶ the approach to family life and issues such as gender roles?

Is it possible for the church to be a genuinely intercultural experience?

Ron Shafer
Drugs man from Weston to Men's Breakfast.

class distinction?
Are we seen as middle class? Old?
Youth see us as nothing to do with them.
Shd we start youthclub?

Filling station?
longer worship block.
not hymn sandwich.
no formal set prayers
modern music.
longer talk.

more accessible to totally unchurched with no baggage?

WORSHIP

Pray for people in your local community, and among your friends and family who belong to different cultures and ethnicities – that all would know the love of God and that your church would be able to reach out to them, welcome them and learn from them.

Start by reading together John's vision of the great multitude in front of God's throne. Group members could then pray for people known to them, and end their prayer with the lines below with everyone joining in the words in bold.

'After this I looked, and there before me was a great multitude that no one could count, from every nation, tribe, people and language, standing before the throne and in front of the Lamb. They were wearing white robes and were holding palm branches in their hands. And they cried out in a loud voice: 'Salvation belongs to our God, who sits on the throne, and to the Lamb.'

Revelation 7:9-10

Use this response after each of your prayers:

Creator God, who includes all people in your family
May our church be a place of welcome and love for every nation, tribe, people and language.

DURING THE WEEK

Choose to expand your experiences of different cultures this week – talk to a friend from a different culture about their upbringing or family traditions; visit shops from different nationalities if there are some nearby; read stories online from a global Christian organisation such as Tearfund, CMS or Compassion; read a theologian from a non-Western country; visit a local church that serves a different people group to yours. Ask God to show you what he wants you to learn from these experiences

FOR FURTHER STUDY

Richard Sudworth's book *Distinctly Welcoming* (Scripture Union) is a very practical guide to churches who want to engage with people from other faiths and cultures.

Anvil, the Anglican evangelical journal for theology and mission, has an online edition reflecting on the Ephesian moment and the need for global theology. It's available at http://anviljournal.org/18 and is free to access – you just need to register.

Read *Water Buffalo Theology* (Orbis Books) by Kosuke Koyama, a Japanese theologian who was one of the twentieth centuries leading voices in bridging Western and non-Western theologies.

Session 3: Rooted in Love

 AIM: To give people an opportunity to linger with Paul's prayer for the Ephesians, to soak in its riches and to understand more of God's love.

TO SET THE SCENE

When have you been aware of God's love in your life? Share experiences, relationships or events that have communicated God's love to you.

The structure of this week is different to the others. You'll have an opportunity to linger with the wonderful prayer that Paul wrote for the Ephesians, using a Bible study method from South Africa. Your group leader will guide you through the study and tell you exactly what to do.

Paul's prayer for the Ephesians is not that they would transform their communities, or convert their neighbours, or fight injustice, or spend hours in prayer, or memorise God's word, or serve the poor.

His prayer was that Christ would live in them, and that they would know they are loved.

READ THE PASSAGE TOGETHER:

3 *¹⁴For this reason I kneel before the Father, ¹⁵from whom every family in heaven and on earth derives its name. ¹⁶I pray that out of his glorious riches he may strengthen you with power through his Spirit in your inner being, ¹⁷so that Christ may dwell in your hearts through faith. And I pray that you, being rooted and established in love, ¹⁸may have power, together with all the Lord's holy people, to grasp how wide and long and high and deep is the love of Christ, ¹⁹and to know this love that surpasses knowledge—that you may be filled to the measure of all the fullness of God.*

²⁰Now to him who is able to do immeasurably more than all we ask or imagine, according to his power that is at work within us, ²¹to him be glory in the church and in Christ Jesus throughout all generations, for ever and ever! Amen.

Ephesians 3:14-21

DURING THE WEEK

Continue to read this passage during the week, asking God to reveal the depth of his love for you. Choose one person that you know needs to grasp the enormity of God's love, and pray these verses intentionally for them each day, naming them in the prayer.

My thoughts and notes....

Session 4: Body of Christ

 AIM: To understand our calling as the body of Christ to continue the ministry of Jesus in our world.

TO SET THE SCENE

Talk about your bodies! Share experiences of using your body really well, of enjoying physical strength and exertion. Share stories of coping with illness or injury, where your body hasn't been able to achieve what you would like.

READ THE PASSAGE TOGETHER:

4 ¹*As a prisoner for the Lord, then, I urge you to live a life worthy of the calling you have received. ²Be completely humble and gentle; be patient, bearing with one another in love. ³Make every effort to keep the unity of the Spirit through the bond of peace. ⁴There is one body and one Spirit, just as you were called to one hope when you were called; 5 one Lord, one faith, one baptism; ⁶one God and Father of all, who is over all and through all and in all.*

⁷*But to each one of us grace has been given as Christ apportioned it. ⁸This is why it says:*

"When he ascended on high,
he took many captives
and gave gifts to his people."

⁹*(What does "he ascended" mean except that he also descended to the lower, earthly regions? ¹⁰He who descended is the very one who ascended higher than all the heavens, in order to fill the whole universe.) ¹¹So Christ himself gave the apostles, the prophets, the evangelists, the pastors and teachers, ¹²to equip his people for works of service, so that the body of Christ may be built up ¹³until we all reach unity in the faith and in the knowledge of the Son of God and become mature, attaining to the whole measure of the fullness of Christ.*

¹⁴*Then we will no longer be infants, tossed back and forth by the waves, and blown here and there by every wind of teaching and by the cunning and craftiness of people in their deceitful scheming. ¹⁵Instead, speaking the truth in love, we will grow to become in every respect the mature body of him who is the head, that is, Christ.*

16From him the whole body, joined and held together by every supporting ligament, grows and builds itself up in love, as each part does its work.

Ephesians 4:1-16

Several times in Ephesians, Paul refers to the Church as the Body of Christ: in 1:23, in 3:6, three times in this passage in v4, v12 and v16 and then again in 4:25, 5:23 and 5:30. We are the continuing presence of Christ in the world; Jesus is here, no longer literally in his own material body, but spiritually and physically in his body, the Church.

DISCUSS TOGETHER

1. According to Paul in verses 1-3, what are the marks of a life that is worthy of the calling we have received?

A Poem

Christ has no body but yours,
No hands, no feet on earth but yours;
Yours are the eyes with which he looks with compassion on this world.
Yours are the feet with which he walks to do good;
Yours are the hands with which he blesses all the world.
Yours are the hands; yours are the feet
Yours are the eyes; you are his body.
Christ has no body now on earth but yours.

St Teresa of Avila

2. What is your understanding of the Church as the Body of Christ? Do you find Teresa of Avila's poem helpful? What value does this view place on our acts of love, or on our failure to serve?

3. Look back at the ministry of Jesus in the gospels. If we are to faithfully embody Christ in the world, what will that look like? What type of people will we be drawn to?

4. We often think of each believer being called to be like Jesus, but the body imagery that Paul uses stresses something slightly different – that together as a Church we embody Jesus. What difference is

My thoughts and notes....

there for you between the phrases 'I should be like Jesus' and 'We should be like Jesus'? Does the thought of being one pixel, rather than trying to be the whole picture, help you?

 5. According to verses 11-13, what is the role of prophets, evangelists, pastors and teachers? How can those who don't have those gifts also help the whole church to become more mature? How good is your church at equipping its people for works of service? What could each of you contribute?

 6. What does it mean to speak the truth in love (verse 15)? Share stories of where someone has done this to you and the impact it had. Does this conflict with Paul's encouragement to make every effort to keep unity through the bond of peace (verse 3)?

7. Three times in Ephesians, Paul uses the phrase the 'fullness of Christ' or the 'fullness of God' – 1:23, 3:19 and 4:13. What do you think this phrase means? How do we attain the fullness of Christ?

 8. To function properly each body part needs to be connected to the other parts of the body and particularly to the head. How can we stay connected to Jesus and to each other in a way that sustains us and helps us be Christ to the world?

WORSHIP

On the outline of a body, take it in turns to name the gifts you have or the ways you feel called to serve Jesus, writing them on an appropriate part of the body. Use this as a basis for your prayers and worship, thanking God for the gifts he has given you, praying that each of you would be faithful in embodying Christ.

DURING THE WEEK

Think about how your church embodies Christ in your local community, and how you contribute to the healthy functioning of the body of Christ. Ask God to show you whether you need to be doing more, or less, so that your church serves effectively as the body of Christ.

FOR FURTHER STUDY

1 Corinthians 12 is another wonderful description of the church as the body of Christ that adds to Paul's teaching on this theme. Spend some time reading and praying through these verses.

Tearfund have some excellent writing on their website on integral mission – the understanding that God calls us to love others completely by meeting all their needs, spiritual, material, emotional and social. www.tearfund.org/en/about_us/how_we_work/why_the_church/

Session 5: Community of the Spirit

 AIM: To understand the role of the Spirit in transforming us to be like Jesus

TO SET THE SCENE

Talk about changes that you have made to your lifestyle – perhaps taking up exercise, keeping an allotment, changing the transport you use, reducing your environmental footprint, eating more healthily. What inspired that change, and what helped you stick to it?

READ THE PASSAGE TOGETHER:

4 *¹⁷So I tell you this, and insist on it in the Lord, that you must no longer live as the Gentiles do, in the futility of their thinking. ¹⁸They are darkened in their understanding and separated from the life of God because of the ignorance that is in them due to the hardening of their hearts. ¹⁹Having lost all sensitivity, they have given themselves over to sensuality so as to indulge in every kind of impurity, and they are full of greed.*

²⁰That, however, is not the way of life you learned ²¹when you heard about Christ and were taught in him in accordance with the truth that is in Jesus. ²²You were taught, with regard to your former way of life, to put off your old self, which is being corrupted by its deceitful desires; ²³to be made new in the attitude of your minds; ²⁴and to put on the new self, created to be like God in true righteousness and holiness.

²⁵Therefore each of you must put off falsehood and speak truthfully to your neighbour, for we are all members of one body. ²⁶"In your anger do not sin": Do not let the sun go down while you are still angry, ²⁷and do not give the devil a foothold. ²⁸Anyone who has been stealing must steal no longer, but must work, doing something useful with their own hands, that they may have something to share with those in need.

²⁹Do not let any unwholesome talk come out of your mouths, but only what is helpful for building others up according to their needs, that it may benefit those who listen. ³⁰And do not grieve the Holy Spirit of God, with whom you were sealed for the day of redemption. ³¹Get rid of all bitterness, rage and anger, brawling and slander, along

with every form of malice. ³²Be kind and compassionate to one another, forgiving each other, just as in Christ God forgave you.

5 ¹Follow God's example, therefore, as dearly loved children ²and walk in the way of love, just as Christ loved us and gave himself up for us as a fragrant offering and sacrifice to God.

³But among you there must not be even a hint of sexual immorality, or of any kind of impurity, or of greed, because these are improper for God's holy people. ⁴Nor should there be obscenity, foolish talk or coarse joking, which are out of place, but rather thanksgiving. ⁵For of this you can be sure: No immoral, impure or greedy person—such a person is an idolater—has any inheritance in the kingdom of Christ and of God. ⁶Let no one deceive you with empty words, for because of such things God's wrath comes on those who are disobedient. ⁷Therefore do not be partners with them.

⁸For you were once darkness, but now you are light in the Lord. Live as children of light ⁹(for the fruit of the light consists in all goodness, righteousness and truth) ¹⁰and find out what pleases the Lord. ¹¹Have nothing to do with the fruitless deeds of darkness, but rather expose them. ¹²It is shameful even to mention what the disobedient do in secret. ¹³But everything exposed by the light becomes visible—and everything that is illuminated becomes a light. ¹⁴This is why it is said:

> "Wake up, sleeper,
> rise from the dead,
> and Christ will shine on you."

¹⁵Be very careful, then, how you live—not as unwise but as wise, ¹⁶making the most of every opportunity, because the days are evil. ¹⁷Therefore do not be foolish, but understand what the Lord's will is. ¹⁸Do not get drunk on wine, which leads to debauchery. Instead, be filled with the Spirit, ¹⁹speaking to one another with psalms, hymns, and songs from the Spirit. Sing and make music from your heart to the Lord, ²⁰always giving thanks to God the Father for everything, in the name of our Lord Jesus Christ.

Ephesians 4:17-5:20

Paul describes the kind of life we should lead, and the kind of life we should reject – but rather than this being a heavy list of dos and don'ts, he reveals what will enable us to live as God desires. Ephesians 5:18 says we are to be filled with the Spirit. The Church is the Community of the Spirit, a community in which God himself dwells. God does not only offer us gifts, he offers us himself. There is nothing God will ever ask us to do for him for which he will not also empower us.

DISCUSS TOGETHER

1. Before we consider Paul's instructions for Christian living, think back over what we have learned from Ephesians so far. What foundations do we need to have in place to make sure we get the right emphasis on how we behave?

2. In these verses, Paul tells us how we should live, and how we should not live, but emphasises the Spirit's role in enabling us to put on our new selves. What do we learn about the Spirit from Paul's teaching in Ephesians? Look at 1:13-14; 2:22; 3:16; 4:3-4 as well as 5:18.

3. Paul describes the Church as the dwelling place of the Spirit in 2:22. What does it mean for the Spirit to be 'at home' among God's people? What challenges does such an image present us with?

4. Think about the 'job description' that the Spirit has in the life of your church. Compose a paragraph together entitled 'The things we expect the Holy Spirit to do in our church.' Then consider what you've read about the Spirit in Ephesians and in other key New Testament passages. Write another paragraph entitled 'The things the New Testament suggests the Holy Spirit will do in our church' What are the differences between the two? How can this gap in expectation become fuel for your prayers in the church?

5. In 4:20 to 5:7, Paul presents us with more contrasts, this time between 'how to live' and 'how not to live'. Make a list under each of these headings of what Paul says. Compare your lists with others in the group. How do you feel about them?

6. Looking at these lists, what do you most need the Spirit's help with either in the way you could be living or the things you could be getting rid of?

7. Paul says we need to be intentional about putting off our old self, and putting on the new self (4:22). How do we do this, so that we cooperate with the work of the Spirit, without falling into the error of thinking we need to change ourselves?

8. Paul urges us to live as children of light in verses 8 to 13. What does this look like in practice?

WORSHIP

Paul says that our worship together should be marked by gratitude. Spend some time thanking God for all he has done in your lives, and for all you have learned through studying his word. Pour out your praise and gratitude to God.

DURING THE WEEK

Start each day by asking God to fill you afresh with his Spirit, to enable you to put off your old self and to put on your new self.

FOR FURTHER STUDY

Encounter the Holy Spirit by Jeannie Morgan (Monarch) from Soul Survivor contains true stories, biblical accounts and simple, practical steps to being empowered by the Spirit.

Session 6: Putting it into Practice

 AIM: To spend time considering how people can put into practice what they've learned about the church from Ephesians.

TO SET THE SCENE

Without naming names, and aiming to be constructive, share what you love most about your church, and what you struggle with most about your church.

READ THE PASSAGE TOGETHER:

5 *[21]Submit to one another out of reverence for Christ.*

[22]Wives, submit yourselves to your own husbands as you do to the Lord. [23]For the husband is the head of the wife as Christ is the head of the church, his body, of which he is the Savior. [24]Now as the church submits to Christ, so also wives should submit to their husbands in everything.

[25]Husbands, love your wives, just as Christ loved the church and gave himself up for her [26]to make her holy, cleansing her by the washing with water through the word, [27]and to present her to himself as a radiant church, without stain or wrinkle or any other blemish, but holy and blameless. [28]In this same way, husbands ought to love their wives as their own bodies. He who loves his wife loves himself. [29]After all, no one ever hated their own body, but they feed and care for their body, just as Christ does the church— [30]for we are members of his body. [31]"For this reason a man will leave his father and mother and be united to his wife, and the two will become one flesh." [32]This is a profound mystery—but I am talking about Christ and the church. [33]However, each one of you also must love his wife as he loves himself, and the wife must respect her husband.

6 *[1]Children, obey your parents in the Lord, for this is right. [2]"Honor your father and mother"—which is the first commandment with a promise— [3]"so that it may go well with you and that you may enjoy long life on the earth."*

[4]Fathers, do not exasperate your children; instead, bring them up in the training and instruction of the Lord.

5Slaves, obey your earthly masters with respect and fear, and with sincerity of heart, just as you would obey Christ. 6Obey them not only to win their favor when their eye is on you, but as slaves of Christ, doing the will of God from your heart. 7Serve wholeheartedly, as if you were serving the Lord, not people, 8because you know that the Lord will reward each one for whatever good they do, whether they are slave or free.

9And masters, treat your slaves in the same way. Do not threaten them, since you know that he who is both their Master and yours is in heaven, and there is no favoritism with him.

10Finally, be strong in the Lord and in his mighty power. 11Put on the full armor of God, so that you can take your stand against the devil's schemes. 12For our struggle is not against flesh and blood, but against the rulers, against the authorities, against the powers of this dark world and against the spiritual forces of evil in the heavenly realms. 13Therefore put on the full armor of God, so that when the day of evil comes, you may be able to stand your ground, and after you have done everything, to stand. 14Stand firm then, with the belt of truth buckled around your waist, with the breastplate of righteousness in place, 15and with your feet fitted with the readiness that comes from the gospel of peace. 16In addition to all this, take up the shield of faith, with which you can extinguish all the flaming arrows of the evil one. 17Take the helmet of salvation and the sword of the Spirit, which is the word of God.

18And pray in the Spirit on all occasions with all kinds of prayers and requests. With this in mind, be alert and always keep on praying for all the Lord's people. 19Pray also for me, that whenever I speak, words may be given me so that I will fearlessly make known the mystery of the gospel, 20for which I am an ambassador in chains. Pray that I may declare it fearlessly, as I should.

21Tychicus, the dear brother and faithful servant in the Lord, will tell you everything, so that you also may know how I am and what I am doing. 22I am sending him to you for this very purpose, that you may know how we are, and that he may encourage you.

23Peace to the brothers and sisters, and love with faith from God the Father and the Lord Jesus Christ. 24Grace to all who love our Lord Jesus Christ with an undying love.

Ephesians 5:21-6:24

Paul ends with his letter with some wisdom on relating well and on resisting evil. We'll end our series by reflecting on how what we've covered over the last few weeks applies to our church. But first let's hear about Paul says about relationships...

DISCUSS TOGETHER

1. Paul begins his advice on relating well with a call to mutual submission. What does it mean to submit to one another? What does mutual submission look like in practice – for wives and husbands, parents and children, those in authority and those under authority?

 2. Paul addresses specific groups of people but from these verses, what should characterise all our relationships with each other?

3. Paul uses the metaphor of armour to show how we can resist evil and stand against the devil's schemes. What does this look like in practice? Talk about how someone who is 'wearing' this armour might behave, or what their character might be.

4. The images of the church we've been thinking about over the last few weeks all highlight its communal nature. Tim Keller writes, 'There is no alternative. You can't live the Christian life without a band of Christian friends, without a family of believers in which to find a place.' Do you agree? What would you say to someone who is determined to be a follower of Jesus but who has been damaged or disillusioned by the church?

 5. We've considered four metaphors for the church:

- the people of God, secure in their identity and involved in the mission of God

- the bride of Christ, a diverse community who are committed to learning from each other

- the body of Christ, being Jesus to the world around us

- the community of the Spirit, transformed by God dwelling in us rather than our own efforts

Which resonated most strongly with you? Which of these do you feel your church is closest to at the moment? Which are you farthest from?

6. An advert for a satnav uses the slogan 'You're not stuck in traffic; you are traffic'. When we're aware of all the challenges of church life and how it could be better, it's perhaps helpful to remind ourselves that 'We're not stuck in church; we are church.' How might this attitude affect how we talk and feel about our church, particularly when we're talking about what could be better?

 7. What could you do as a group to help your church get closer to the vibrant, secure, missional community of believers that Paul describes in Ephesians? Listen to everyone's ideas and then decide on one practical step you could take together. Make some plans for how you can carry it out.

WORSHIP

Paul ends his letter with an exhortation to 'pray in the Spirit on all occasions with all kinds of prayers and requests' and to 'be alert and always keep on praying for all the Lord's people.' Spend some time in prayer for individual members of the group and the issues that have been raised for them through these sessions; pray for your church that it would be a vibrant, secure, missional community of believers; and pray for the steps you want to take to bless your church.

FOR FURTHER STUDY

There are different understandings within the church about what Paul means when he says the husband is the head of the wife in Ephesians 5:23.

The Gender Agenda (IVP) by Lis Goddard and Clare Hendry is an excellent book that explores different readings of this and other passages in the Bible that relate to men and women.

Leaders' Guide

TO HELP YOU LEAD

You may have led a group many times before or this may be your first time. Here is some advice on how to lead these studies.

- As a group leader, you don't have to be an expert or a lecturer. You are there to facilitate the learning of the group members – helping them to discover for themselves the wisdom in God's word. You should not be doing most of the talking or dishing out the answers, whatever the group expects from you!

- You do need to be aware of the group's dynamics, however. People can be quite quick to label themselves and each other in a group situation. One person might be seen as the expect, another the moaner who always has something to complain about. One person may be labelled as quiet and not expected to contribute; another person may always jump in with something to say. Be aware of the different type of individuals in the group, but don't allow the labels to stick. You may need to encourage those who find it hard to get a word in, and quieten down those who always have something to say. Talk to members between sessions to find out how they feel about the group.

- The sessions are planned to try and engage every member in active learning. Of course you cannot force anyone to take part if they don't want to, but it won't be too easy to be a spectator. Activities that ask everyone to write down a word, or talk in twos, and then report back to the group are there for a reason. They give everyone space to think and form their opinion, even if not everyone voices it out loud.

- Do adapt the sessions for your group as you feel is appropriate. Some groups may know each other very well and will be prepared to talk at a deep level. New groups may take a bit of time to get to know each other before making themselves vulnerable, but encourage members to share their lives with each other.

- You probably won't be able to tackle all the questions in each session so decide in advance which ones are most appropriate to your group and situation.

▶ Encourage a number of replies to each question. The study is not about finding a single right answer, but about sharing experiences and thoughts in order to find out how to apply the Bible to people's lives. When brainstorming, don't be too quick to evaluate the contributions. Write everything down and then have a look to see which suggestions are worth keeping.

▶ Similarly, encourage everyone to ask questions, voice doubts and discuss difficulties. Some parts of the Bible are difficult to understand. Sometimes the Christian faith throws up paradoxes. Painful things happen to us that make it difficult to see what God is doing. A group should be a safe place to express all of this. If discussion doesn't resolve the issue, send everyone away to pray about it between sessions, and ask your minister for advice.

▶ Give yourself time in the week to read through the Bible passage and the questions. Read the Leaders' notes for the session, as different ways of presenting the questions are sometimes suggested. However during the session don't be too quick to come in with the answer – sometimes people need space to think.

▶ Delegate as much as you like! The easiest activities to delegate are reading the text, and the worship sessions, but there are other ways to involve the group members. Giving people responsibility can help them own the session much more.

▶ Pray for group members by name, that God would meet with them during the week. Pray for the group session, for a constructive and helpful time. Ask the Lord to equip you as you lead the group.

THE STRUCTURE OF EACH SESSION

Feedback: find out what people remember from the previous session, or if they have been able to act during the week on what was discussed last time.

To set the scene: an activity or question to get everyone thinking about the subject to be studied.

Bible reading: it's important actually to read the passage you are studying during the session. Ask someone to prepare this in advance or go around the group reading a verse or two each. Don't assume everyone will be happy to read out loud.

Questions and activities: adapt these as appropriate to your group. Some groups may enjoy a more activity-based approach; some may prefer just to discuss the questions. Try out some new things!

Worship: suggestions for creative worship and prayer are included, which give everyone an opportunity to respond to God, largely individually. Use these alongside singing or other group expressions of worship. Add a prayer time with opportunities to pray for group members and their families and friends.

For next week: this gives a specific task to do during the week, helping people to continue to think about or apply what they have learned.

Further study: suggestions are given for those people who want to study the themes further. These could be included in the group if you feel it's appropriate and if there is time.

WHAT YOU NEED

A list of materials that are needed is printed at the start of each session in the Leaders' Guide. In addition you will probably need:

Bibles: the main Bible passage is printed in the book so that all the members can work from the same version. It is useful to have other Bibles available, or to ask everyone to bring their own, so that other passages can be referred to.

Paper and pens: for people who need more space than is in the book!

Flip chart: it is helpful to write down people's comments during a brainstorming session, so that none of the suggestions is lost. There may not be space for a proper flip chart in the average lounge, and having one may make it feel too much like a business meeting or lecture. Try getting someone to write on a big sheet of paper on the floor or coffee table, and then stick this up on the wall with blu-tack.

GROUND RULES

How do people know what is expected of them in a group situation? Is it ever discussed, or do we just pick up clues from each other? You may find it helpful to discuss some ground rules for the group at the start of this course, even if your group has been going a long time. This also gives you an opportunity to talk about how you, as the leader, see the group. Ask everyone to think about what they want to get out of the course. How do they want the group to work? What values do they want to be part of the group's experience; honesty, respect, confidentiality? How do they want their contributions to be treated? You could ask everyone to write down three ground rules on slips of paper and put them in a bowl. Pass the bowl around the group. Each person takes out a rule and reads it, and someone collates the list. Discuss the ground rules that have been suggested and come up with a top five. This method enables everyone to contribute fairly anonymously. Alternatively, if your group are all quite vocal, have a straight discussion about it!

NB Not all questions in each session are covered, some are self-explanatory.

ICONS

 The aim of the session

 Investigate what else the Bible says

 How does this apply to me?

 What about my church?

 Engaging with the world

Session 1: Notes - People of God

YOU WILL NEED

- A local map. Try to find one that includes the areas where members of your group live, work, study, shop and socialise. Have some highlighter pens for people to mark the map, or small post-it notes and pens if you would prefer the map to stay pristine.

- Write the 'before' phrases in question 6 on a piece of paper each for the worship. You'll need pens for the group; brightly coloured ones would be good.

- It's helpful for each member of the group to have a Bible as well as a workbook.

TO SET THE SCENE

This gets people thinking about their identity, and can be a way to find out new things about each other. It provides a way into looking at our identity in Christ which is the focus of this week's passage.

DISCUSS TOGETHER

1. Some versions of the Bible will use the word 'saints' rather than 'people of God'. We belong to God and are loved by God. God is not remote or uninterested in us; God chooses to be in relationship with us. He is not ashamed to call us his own!

2. This is the list I came up with:

I am blessed.
I am chosen; I am holy; I am blameless.
I am loved; I am predestined/chosen in advance; I am adopted into God's family.
I am freely given God's grace.
I am redeemed; I am forgiven; I am lavished with God's grace.
I have God's will revealed to me.
I am chosen and predestined; I am for the praise of his glory.
I am included in Christ; I am saved.
I am marked with the Holy Spirit.
I am an heir of God; I am the possession of God.

3. In all your discussions about your church during these studies, encourage people not to moan or gossip, but to talk constructively, lovingly, honestly and respectfully – and above all to pray for the church.

4. He prays that they would know the hope to which they are called, the inheritance they have to look forward to, and the power of God for us who believe. Again, Paul wants them to be secure in their identity, and looking forward to what God will do.

5. Encourage people to name the institutions and corporations that seem to dominate our world as well as more personal ones – the government, the UN, banks and the financial sector, my boss! We need to remind ourselves that Jesus rules over all these things.

6. The 'before' list might include:

> Dead; sinful; disobedient; following the world; ruled by sinful nature; deserving wrath.

The 'after' list might include:

> Alive in Christ; loved by God; saved by grace; raised with Christ; seated with Christ; God's handiwork; given purpose.

7. Someone who thinks they have been saved by works will be compelled to keep doing good for their own benefit, will feel they have to earn their salvation, might worry that they could lose it, could be judgemental of those who don't do the same.

Someone who knows they have been saved by grace will be filled with gratitude, will be secure in their salvation, will want to bless God and others by doing good, and will accept others who make mistakes.

8. We are created to do good works, prepared for us in advance. This doesn't contradict the fact we are saved by grace; those good works don't earn us God's love, they enable us to contribute to God's mission in the world.

Encourage people to think widely about the mission of God. God is not just interested in seeing people join the church, but longs to redeem the whole of creation. A helpful measure of the scope of God's mission has been the identification of different spheres of society and culture, sometimes referred to as the '7 mountains' of culture: business, government, media, arts and entertainment, education, the family and religion. To these can be added the vital spheres of science and technology. What would our world be like if the rule and reign of Christ was fully seen in each of these spheres?

9. If people's spheres of influence aren't actually on the map, write them at the edges! Look out for 'clusters' of influence – areas that you have in common. Point out the range of connections that just this one small group has. Use this map in the future for your prayers and action as a group.

WORSHIP

Spread out the 'before' phrases that you have written on paper. Invite people to pray and transform these phrases into the 'after' that the passage describes. They can do this by turning the paper over, and writing something different, or by using the pens to alter the 'before' phrases. You will end up with a visual transformation that mirrors what Christ has done in us.

DURING THE WEEK

Encourage people to immerse themselves in Ephesians 1:3-14 during the week, and allow the words to soak in.

Session 2: Notes - Bride of Christ

YOU WILL NEED

If there are people from different ethnic backgrounds and languages in your group, think about how you might involve them in this session. They could pray in their mother tongue for example, talk about church life in their home country or share food from their culture.

TO SET THE SCENE

This activity reveals how much interaction people have with different cultures. Some parts of the UK are very multicultural while others are more monocultural, so expect to see your local context reflected in your groups' responses.

DISCUSS TOGETHER

1. Paul uses these phrases: brought near by the blood of Christ (v13); made the two one, and destroyed the barrier v14); create one humanity out of the two (v15); reconcile them to God, putting to death their hostility (v16); both have access to the Father by one Spirit (v18); fellow-citizens with God's people and members of God's household (v19); built together into a holy temple (v20-22).

2. God told Abraham that he would be made into a great nation and that all peoples would be blessed through him (Genesis 12:1-3). The Jews understood themselves to be God's chosen people, with an exclusive relationship with God. If others wanted to join them they had to become fully Jewish. Jesus healed the servant of a ~~Centurion~~ Roman. (Luke 7:1), and the daughter of a ~~Canaanite~~ Pagan woman (Matthew 15:21-28). He taught the Samaritan woman and empowered her to be an evangelist; most Jews considered the Samaritans to be of a different religion, although their faith shared many roots.

4. Challenges are each thinking that their way of doing things is the only way or the right way! Benefits are a richer understanding of who God is, through learning how other people relate to God. People need to be generous, humble, teachable, discerning and not controlling.

6. Churches can create opportunities by looking for local links - connecting with churches which have a different ethnic makeup through joint projects, inviting in speakers, and even worshipping together. Or by looking for global links – investing in twinning or exchange programmes, and facilitating visits to other countries.

7 and 8. These questions are not intended to engender guilt or to suggest that churches can be changed quickly. But see if you can come up with some practical suggestions for your church to be more like the one that John describes in Revelation, with 'every nation, tribe, people and language.'

WORSHIP

If your group is not used to praying responsively like this, you could ask someone in advance to lead the way showing how this response should be used at the end of their prayer.

DURING THE WEEK

Some people might find it easier to approach these activities together, so do encourage them to pair up.

Session 3: Notes - Rooted in Love

This session is quite different in format to all the others in the book. Paul's fantastic prayer for the Ephesians is worth dwelling on and you'll use a method of Bible study from South Africa called the Lumko method which encourages a slow, prayerful way of reading scripture but also enables people to talk about how the passage applies to them.

You will need to lead the Bible study using the following structure, so read it through a few times to familiarise yourself with the different stages. Reassure people that you will guide them through each stage and tell them exactly what to do. Some of the stages invite group members to contribute by praying or reading; you could set this up in advance or simply wait for someone to respond at the time. It helps if everyone is using the same version of the Bible so encourage people to use the printed version in this booklet.

This study will take anywhere from 30 minutes to over an hour depending on how many there are in your group and how responsive people are. Try to resist filling any spare time with further study or anything new, so that people can stay focused on the passage.

Start with the 'set the scene' activity to get people talking. Then follow this structure for the rest of the session, announcing the title of each step as you go through.

STEP ONE – WE INVITE THE LORD

Invite someone in the group to pray, thanking God for his presence with you, and asking God to speak through his word.

STEP TWO – WE READ THE TEXT

Invite someone to read the text to the group, slowly. Allow a moment's silence afterwards.

STEP THREE – WE DWELL ON THE TEXT

Invite people to read the passage again to themselves and then to read aloud a word or a phrase from the passage that strikes them, without commenting on it. Others in the group should listen and then repeat the words to themselves silently, leaving a pause before someone else contributes. In this way, you will hear most of the passage read again. It doesn't matter if people repeat what others have said; in fact it can highlight what God is saying to the group.

STEP FOUR – WE ARE QUIET

Explain first that someone will read the whole text one more time, and then leave a period of silence. Tell people how long the silence will be – perhaps three minutes if people are not used to being silent, or longer if you think they will appreciate it. Encourage people to be open to God in the silence. Then invite someone to read the text.

STEP FIVE – WE SHARE WHAT WE HAVE HEARD IN OUR HEARTS

Invite people to talk about what struck them from the text, what questions it raised, what they felt God say to them through the text. Encourage everyone to contribute.

STEP SIX – WE SEARCH TOGETHER

Gently move the conversation on and get people talking about how these verses apply to them. What response does this passage require from us? How might it change us? What do we need to do?

STEP SEVEN – WE PRAY TOGETHER

Spend some time in prayer bringing to God the things you have talked about, and asking for his help.

End the session by encouraging people to pray this prayer for others during the week, as outlined at the end of the session in the front of the booklet.

Session 4: Notes - Body of Christ

If appropriate to your denomination, it would be very fitting to celebrate communion together at the end of this session, sharing the bread that Jesus describes as his body broken for us.

YOU WILL NEED

- A large sheet of paper with the outline of a body on it, plus some coloured pens.

- Bread and wine to celebrate communion, if appropriate, with liturgy if you want to use it.

TO SET THE SCENE

Talking about how we use our bodies well, or suffer when they aren't fit, will resonate with people as they talk about being the body of Christ together. Of course, be sensitive to those who are uncomfortable with their bodies.

DISCUSS TOGETHER

1. To be humble, gentle, patient, bearing with one another, keeping the unity of the Spirit.

2. When we serve others we do it as Jesus. If we don't play our part then we limit what Christ can do in our world.

3. You could split the group into twos and threes and give each one of the gospels to look through and then report back on. Jesus spent time with 'tax collectors and sinners' – those considered to be outcasts in his society. He chose disciples that others had overlooked as leaders. He was not afraid to challenge the rich and powerful, including the religious leaders of his day.

4. Remind people of 1 Corinthians 12 where Paul also talks about the body of Christ and emphasises the different roles that people have to play.

5. Not all of us are apostles or teachers, but we all have a responsibility to grow to maturity together. It's important that we each play our part, rather than expecting our church leaders to do it all for us.

6. Sometimes the idea of 'speaking the truth in love' can be abused and be a euphemism for being rude or unkind! But used correctly it's really valuable and is something that helps us grow. As people discuss this, acknowledge where it might have been misused, and encourage people to see the immense value in having people who are not afraid to lovingly challenge, encourage and correct us.

7. Although we will never be exactly like Jesus in this life, Paul encourages us to aspire to be as full of God as it is possible for a person to be. It's something we can pray for God to do in us.

8. Practices such as prayer, meeting together like this, studying God's word and worshipping together can all keep us connected to Jesus and to each other. Affirm the diversity in the group by encouraging people to say what they personally find helpful.

WORSHIP

Some will find it easier than others to articulate their gifts and the way they serve Christ, but emphasise the fact that everyone does have a part to play and encourage people away from false modesty. Writing on different parts of the body highlights the different roles people have to play; people with gifts of speaking/ teaching might write theirs on the head or mouth. People who care for others might write theirs on the hands or heart and so on. If people genuinely don't know how they can serve or use their gifts, make that a springboard for prayer, that God would reveal to them the part he wants them to play.

Session 5: Notes - Community of the Spirit

YOU WILL NEED

▶ It would be helpful to have paper and pens for the 'job description' for the Holy Spirit.

TO SET THE SCENE

Draw out the role that other people have played in encouraging group members to stick to their good intentions.

DISCUSS TOGETHER

1. Paul says we need to be rooted and established in love in Ephesians 3:17. Chapter one focuses on our identity in Christ and all God has done for us. 2:8 reminds us that we are saved by grace not works.

2. Ephesians 1:13 says the Holy Spirit is a seal, showing we belong to God, and a deposit guaranteeing what is to come.

2:22 says that the church is the dwelling place of God by his Spirit.

3:16 says that God will strengthen us with power through his Spirit in our inner being.

4:3-4 emphasises that there is one Spirit who unites us.

5:18 says that God will fill us with his Spirit.

3. Are we a suitable dwelling place for God's Spirit? Will God feel at home with us?

4. Other passages you might consider are John 14:15-29; Acts 1:6-9 and 2:1-4; Romans 8:1-17; Galatians 5:16-26. Share this out between different members of the group and get them to pool their thoughts.

5. How to live:

Speak truthfully; use your hands constructively; share with those in need; build others up; be kind and compassionate; be forgiving; live a life of love; be thankful.

How not to live:

Put off falsehood; do not sin in anger; don't give the devil a foothold;

don't steal; don't speak in an unwholesome way; don't grieve the Spirit; get rid of bitterness, rage, anger, brawling, slander and malice; flee sexual immorality, impurity and greed; shun obscenity, foolish talk and coarse joking; don't be immoral, impure, greedy, idolatrous, or deceived!

6. This question invites people to be honest and to make themselves vulnerable to others in the group. The degree to which people are happy to do this will depend on how well they know each other, and also what is modelled by the leaders.

7. Focusing our prayers on our need for the Spirit to transform us is one way.

8. Living in the light is about being honest, open, vulnerable and about making ourselves appropriately accountable to each other. Invite people to share their own experiences of having a prayer partner, mentor or spiritual director.

Session 6: Notes - Putting it into Practice

Some of this week's passage talks about the relationship between husbands and wives. Christians come to different conclusions about what Paul means when he says the husband is the head of the wife, so to keep the conversation focused on the theme of this series that issue isn't directly addressed in this study. If people want to explore that more, point them towards the book recommended at the end of the session – *The Gender Agenda* by Lis Goddard and Clare Hendry.

TO SET THE SCENE

Again this has the potential to be quite negative, so encourage people not to get personal and to remember that they are members of the church that they are talking about!

DISCUSS TOGETHER

1. To submit means to yield or surrender to the will or authority of someone else. A beautiful example of submission is Jesus in the Garden of Gethsemane praying to God 'not my will but your be done.' (Luke 22:42) Submitting to one another means to lay down our need to be right or to control. It's a voluntary, loving act that recognises the integrity and value of the other person.

2. Love, submission, honour, service are some of the characteristics we can draw from these verses.

3. Someone who has the 'belt of truth buckled on' will speak the truth and value the truth; they will be righteous; they will have faith and be faithful; they will be secure in their salvation; they will know God's word; they'll be ready to share the gospel and talk about what Jesus has done. If we live like this, we will find it easier to resist evil and take a stand against the devil's schemes.

4. We need to listen to people who have been hurt by the church, but also understand how significant our involvement can be in helping them feel differently about the church.

6. In all our comments about the church, we need to remember that we are the church; we're probably part of the problem and we can definitely be part of the solution.

7. Encourage people to share lots of ideas and keep a note of them. Choose something that is practical, achievable and measurable so you will know when it's happened!